MAYAN LEGENDS

THE MOST FASCINATING MAYA LEGENDS
FOR READERS OF ALL AGES

ADAPTATION, TEXT
AND ILLUSTRATIONS
JAVIER COVO TORRES

Mayan Legends

La Xtabay
Maquech
El Enano de Uxmal
Nicte Há
Zamná

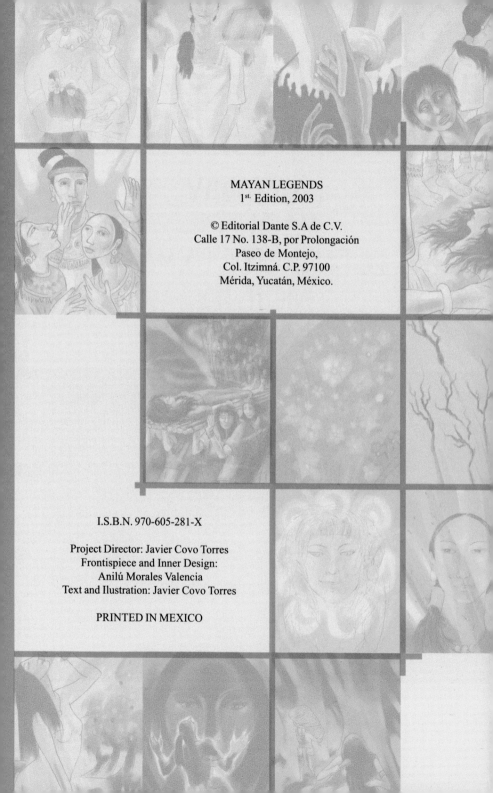

MAYAN LEGENDS
1st. Edition, 2003

© Editorial Dante S.A de C.V.
Calle 17 No. 138-B, por Prolongación
Paseo de Montejo,
Col. Itzimná. C.P. 97100
Mérida, Yucatán, México.

I.S.B.N. 970-605-281-X

Project Director: Javier Covo Torres
Frontispiece and Inner Design:
Anilú Morales Valencia
Text and Ilustration: Javier Covo Torres

PRINTED IN MEXICO

To Yucatan,
THE MAGICAL LAND OF THE MAYA

INTRODUCTION

Throughout the centuries the Mayan legends, and all stories of the fabulous beings populating Maya mythology, have become a fascinating literature rivaling that of other great cultures. It is a literature that can be read and enjoyed by children and adults alike. It is also a magical literature deeply rooted in the life, habits and traditions of the contemporary Maya of the Yucatan Peninsula.

Even today, rural campesinos believe in the existence of mythical beings. The Xtabay, a succubus or evil dwarf woman that sets romantic traps for young men with the object of hurting or killing them, is still feared, and great respect is afforded the mischievous Aluxes, little beings capable of the bloodiest deeds or, if given certain offerings, of acts of goodwill towards the people living in the towns and haciendas of Yucatan. There are many, many more fabulous beings like the Xtabay or the Aluxes that populate the austere life of the Mayan campesino, and terrify him during the quiet Yucatecan nights. Maybe it is the progress now experienced in even the most rural towns, or the migration of campesinos to the large cities, or perhaps the negative influence of foreign customs on our values and traditions, but, whatever the cause, these beautiful, singular ancient myths and legends are being diluted and forgotten, slowly leaching the substance from our Maya-Yucatecan culture.

In response to this worrying loss of our mythological traditions, and thus of our indigenous literature and anthropology, the editors at Editorial Dante studied and analyzed the situation, and decided to restore this rural legendary memory and offer it to their readers. The resulting stories are intended especially for children and have a simple style free of unnecessary rhetoric. They are attractively and beautifully illustrated in vibrant color that will make the reading of these famous Maya legends all the more enjoyable.

The first titles in the series will be the legends of the Xtabay; Maquech; Zamná: the discovery of henequen; Nicte-Ha: White Flower; and the famous old woman and the Dwarf of Uxmal. This last is one the oldest known legend, and was first heard around 1840 by the illustrious North American explorer John L. Stephens from some of his Maya workers during his travels in Yucatan.

In writing out these legends the greatest care has been taken to keep them brief but also to make them fun to read so children can easily understand the warm, human message within each of these stories. The project director and writer of the text, Javier Covo Torres, has also created impelling illustrations to accompany the legends.

Our hope is that we can make the old pedagogic axiom of "learning through fun" a reality by helping children to enjoy these legends. If, while enjoying the stories, the reader also learns and comes to cherish part of the fascinating literature of the ancient Maya, our efforts will have been a success.

Roldán Peniche Barrera.

MAYAN LEGENDS
THE XTABAY

There once lived two beautiful women, *Xkeban* and *Utz-Colel*.
Xkeban, which means "sinner" in Maya, was treated badly because
she committed the sin of love. The townspeople hated her so much
that they had even tried to kick her out of town.

Utz-Colel, which means "good woman" in Maya, was more virtuous than anyone else in town and all her neighbors thought well of her.

Utz-Colel was selfish and had a hard heart. She thought the poor were inferior to her and the sick disgusted her. She was not a sinner but her heart was as cold as a snake's skin.

Xkeban, the sinner, sympathized with beggars and cared for sick people that had been abandoned. She always did good things, never gossiped about others and quietly suffered people's insults.

One morning the town streets filled with an intoxicating perfume that hung in the air for many days. When the neighbors followed the scent they were surprised to find it lead to *Xkeban's* house.

Inside, they found that *Xkeban* had died and the mysterious fragrance that floated through town emanated from her lifeless body. *Utz-Colel* warned the townspeople that this was a demon's trick to fool men.

The people believed *Utz-Colel* and no one, except the poor and invalid who knew her goodness, accompanied her funeral procession. As the funeral went through town it left a trail of the exquisite fragrance of invisible flowers everywhere it passed.

The next day all were surprised to find *Xkeban's* grave covered with wildflowers exalting in the beauty of the new day, but no one ever knew who put the flowers there.

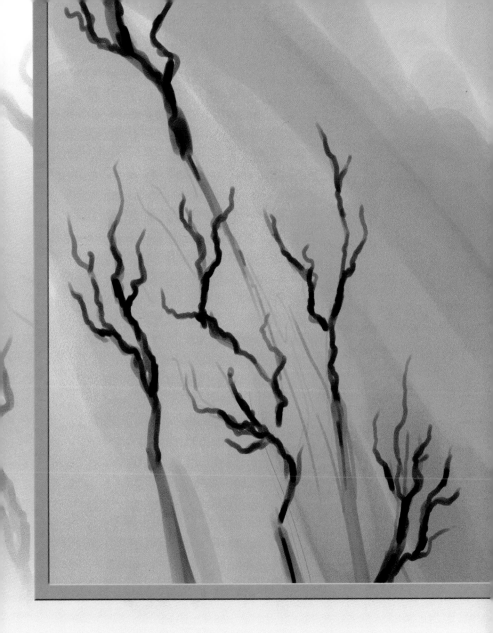

A short time later *Utz-Colel* also died, but from her lifeless body there arose a foul odor. She was mourned for her great virtue and the whole town went to her funeral, but no matter how many flowers they put on her grave, there were never any there the next day.

Xkeban became the flower called Xtabentún, a sweet little flower with a scent as intoxicating as *Xkeban's* love.

Utz-Colel became the flower called Tzacam, a flower with no scent that comes from a cactus as spiny as *Utz-Colel's* soul.

When *Utz-Colel* found herself changed into the Tzacam flower, she thought that *Xkeban's* sins of love were the cause of all the good things that happened to her. So Utz-Colel decided to devote herself to love. She did not understand, however, that *Xkeban* loved from the goodness in her heart, while she, *Utz-Colel*, was bad and perverse, and could give nothing but tainted love.

22

With the help of some evil spirits, *Utz-Colel* worked the marvel of returning to the world in the form of a woman. She wanted to win the hearts of men with her ill-fated, cold love that cut like the cold blades in her heart.

This woman is the *Xtabay*, the flower of the rigid, spiny Tzacam cactus. The *Xtabay* comes back to life and waits for travelers to come by while she patiently combs her black hair behind the ceiba tree. When they see her, she seduces them and then kills them in the fire of her infernal passion.

Mayan Legends
MAQUECH

There was once a beautiful princess with hair like the wings of swallows, and she was called *Cuzán*, which means "swallow" in Maya. Her beauty was legendary and stories were told of her throughout the kingdom and even beyond the walls of the sacred city of Yaxchilán.

Cuzán was the favorite daughter of Ahnú Dtundtunxcaán, the Great Lord submerged in the heavens. She was cheerful and happy; with a face that shined like the sun when her father brought her the most precious of his war spoils.

When *Cuzán* was old enough to marry, her father arranged a marriage between her and prince *Ek Chapat*, son of the Halach Uinic of the great city of Nan Chan, and future Lord of the Kingdom. Cuzán accepted her father's choice, for the moment.

One day, however, after returning from war, the king sent his war spoils to *Cuzán*. When Cuzán went to the Great Palace to thank her father for the resplendent gift, she found him accompanied by *Chalpol*, which means "redhead" in Maya, a handsome young man with hair the color of fire.

When they saw each other, their souls were trapped in a fiery bond. Cuzán's jumping heart could only calmed by the name *"Chalpol"*. They promised never to forget each other and desperately fell into each other's arms under the sacred ceiba tree where the gods hear mortals' prayers.

The entire city knew that *Cuzán* had been promised to prince *Ek Chapat* from Nan Chan, so when the king found out that *Chalpol* was his daughter's lover, he ordered him to be sacrificed. *Cuzán* begged her father to pardon the young man's life, but all in vane.

On the day of the sacrifice, *Chalpol* was painted blue for the sacrifice ceremony. All was prepared and the scent of copal incense burned to keep away spirits wafted out the temple entrance.

With tearful eyes, *Cuzán* again pleaded with her father not to sacrifice Chalpol, promising to never see him again and to obediently accept the prince of Nan Chan as her husband.

After consulting with the priests, the king pardoned the young man's life, but under the condition that his daughter be confined in her rooms. If she came out, *Chalpol* would be sacrificed. Obeying, the princess stayed in her lonely bedroom, with no choice but to dream of *Chalpol*.

That night she was called before the king. As she entered the temple
patio her eyes searched for those of her lover, and when she did not see
them she trembled to think that he might have been sacrificed.

She asked her father what had happened to *Chalpol*, but he only smiled.
A sorcerer then came to her with a beetle and said, *Cuzán*, here you
have *Chalpol*. Your father granted him his life, but asked me to turn
him into an insect as punishment for having the audacity to love you".

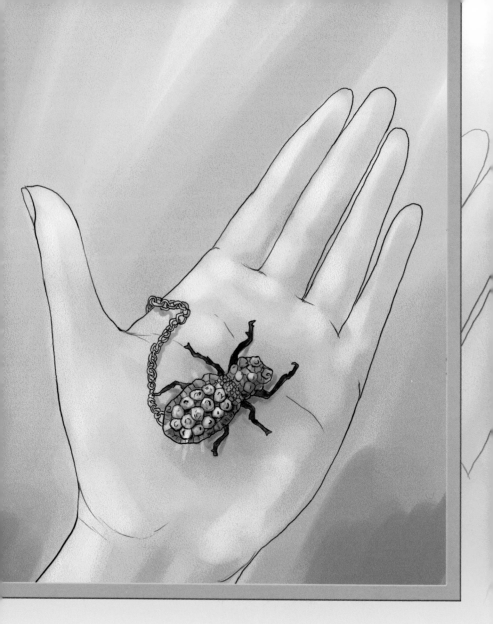

Princess Cuzán took the beetle and said, "I promised never to separate from you and I now I can fulfill my promise".
The best jeweler in the kingdom covered the beetle with precious stones and fixed a gold chain to one of its legs.

Cuzán then pinned the chained beetle to her dress and said, "Maquech, you are the man I love. With you here close to my heart you will always hear it beating for you and never forget my eternal promise to never forget you. Maquech, the man I love, here on my breast you will live the eternal pain of my not having you.

"Maquech, the man I love, the gods have never known a love so
intense and alive as that that burns in my soul for you". Princess
Cuzán and her lover *Chalpol*, now changed into a maquech beetle,
loved with an overflowing, timeless love.

Mayan Legends

The Dwarf of
Uxmal

In the city of Kabah there once lived an old witch that knew the mysteries of the stars and the secrets of herbs. Every day she would spend time sweetly watching a very small egg she had found one day.

One day the egg cracked and out came a baby that was the light of her life. The baby talked and knew many marvelous things about the world. The baby was a dwarf and as the years went by he aged and his beard and hair grew, but his body stayed the same small size.

The old witch spent the better part of her time by the fireplace, where she jealously guarded a drum made of a tree trunk, called a tunkul, which she had hidden there. One time, the shrewd and malicious dwarf saw that the witch had wandered away and he found the tunkul in the fireplace ashes.

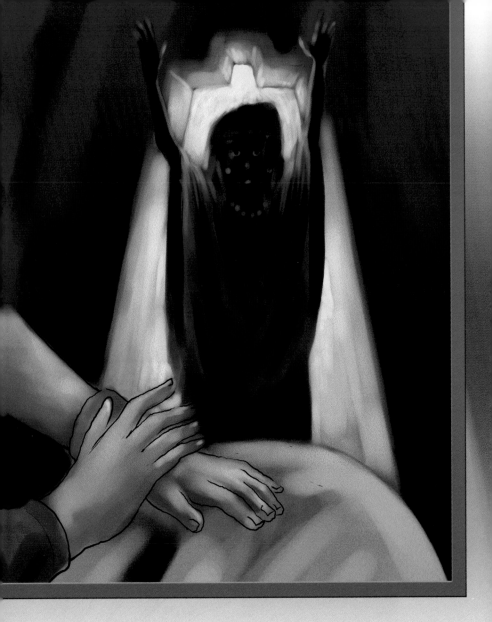

He began to beat on the tunkul so strongly that it sounded far and wide. When she heard the sound the old witch rushed back and told him that what he had done would change the course of history and that he would be involved in terrible things.

The tunkul's sound had traveled as far as the king's palace at Uxmal. Everyone knew that this sound announced the end of his reign, but his councilors said that if he could find who had beat the tunkul he could ask him the truth that he needed to change the laws of destiny.

The king ordered that he who had beat the tunkul be brought before him. When his guards arrived at Kabah they found out the dwarf had sounded the tunkul, so they took him to the king's palace at Uxmal.

The king asked the dwarf if there was some way he could free himself from the terrible prophecy. The dwarf told him that he should build a road from Uxmal to Kabah and when the road reached Kabah he would return with the answer.

The king had the road built and when it reached Kabah the dwarf and the old witch came to Uxmal. They told the king that he would have his desired answer if he passed a test in which a hard little fruit, called a cocoyol, was broken over his head and the dwarf's. The king accepted under the condition that the dwarf undergo the test first. The dwarf accepted.

The executioner put the cocoyol on the dwarf's head and gave it a brutally hard blow, but the dwarf just stood up and smiled. The king then climbed up the scaffold to undergo the test. The executioner's first blow killed the king.

And so the dwarf was proclaimed king of Uxmal.
The same day the old witch sent for the dwarf to tell him that she
would soon die. But, she said, she would die happy because he was
now king.

She gave him much sage advice. "Work justly and always face the truth, but remember it is more important to be good than to be just". "Obey the voices of the gods, but listen to the voices of men". "Never disdain the poor and always distrust the powerful".

For many years the dwarf followed her wise words and the city of Uxmal was peaceful, prosperous and happy. With time, however, the dwarf began to commit excesses and became tyrannical and proud.

In his pride he had a clay statue made and placed over a fire so that it might be more powerful than his own gods. The statue, though, was hardened by the fire and began to vibrate like a bell. This made the people believe the statue spoke and they began to worship it.

The gods were indignant at this sacrilege and decided to punish the
city by sending thousands of warriors to attack it. These warriors
sacked and burned the city, forever erasing the memory of the people
and the dwarf that once ruled over them.

MAYAN LEGENDS
NICTE HÁ
LOTUS FLOWER

In the deepest forests of the Maya there was once a marvelous kingdom reigned over by a prince called Chacdziedzib, which means "red bird" in Maya. The prince was deeply in love with the daughter of the guardian of the Sacred Cenote, a beauty called *Nicte-Há*, which means "water flower" in Maya.

Chacdziedzib wore a red tunic and was loved and venerated by his people. He was a valiant and gallant warrior and a flawless shot with his bow and arrow.

Before dawn the prince always went looking for his beloved *Nicte-Há* at the edge of the Sacred Cenote. As the dawn broke into the sky with rays of sun, the air filled with his words of love for her.

The Great Priest, however, was convinced that *Chacdziedzib* should marry a king's daughter and was opposed to his love for *Nicte-Há*. He brought together the great lords and they decided that the daughter of the guardian of the Sacred Cenote should die.

But the court jester had heard everything and ran straight to tell the prince the decision. Prince *Chacdziedzib* ordered his finest warrior to find *Nicte-Há* and bring her to the Royal Palace, where he would marry her.

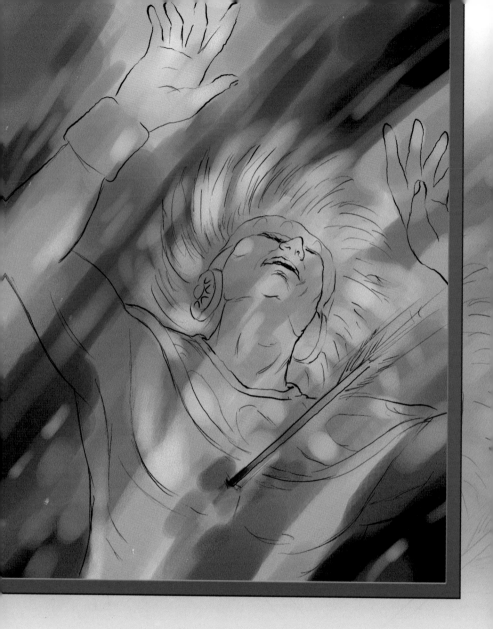

The noble warrior left on his mission but was ambushed and killed in the black night and his body thrown into the forest.

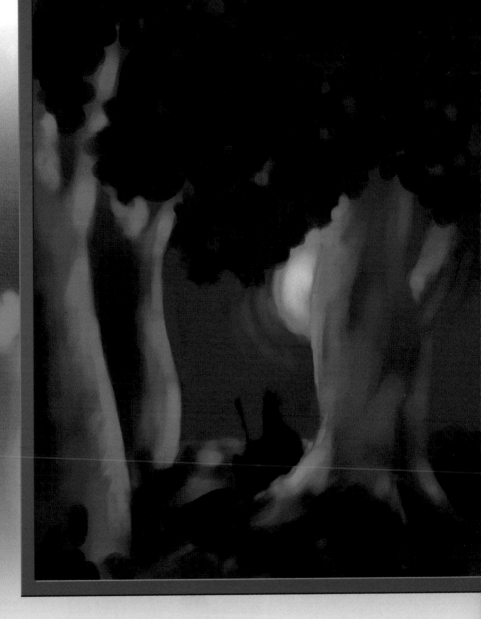

Again, the jester saw it all. When the prince of the red tunic was told
what had happened, he took his bow and arrows and went straight to
the Sacred Cenote in search of his beloved. That night he stood guard
under the ceiba trees.

At dawn, when *Nicte-Há* went to admire herself in the placid waters of the Cenote, the prince came to her and wrapped his arms around her. He loved her with all his might.

But from the shadows flew an arrow that pierced the beautiful damsel's chest. Her fragile, lifeless body fell into the Sacred Cenote and sunk into the waters where the gods lived.

Prince *Chacdziedzib* watched as the body of his beloved disappeared into the depths. All that remained was the dress of *Nicte-Há* floating on the still waters of the Cenote.

He was wounded to his soul and pleaded for pity and compassion from the gods as he bathed himself in tears. Such was his pain that his heart burst into pieces and he fell into a pool of his own blood, agonizing, at the edge of the Sacred Cenote.

The gods heard *Chacdziedzib* and sent the Lord of Waters and the Lord of Birds to the Cenote.

The Lord of Waters dove into the depths of the Cenote and turned *Nicte-Há's* inert body into a fabulous lotus flower.

The Lord of Birds put his hands on the prince's heart and gave it wings, turning it into a handsome red bird, a cardinal always thirsty for love.

From this time on, when dawn breaks, a red bird descends into the Sacred Cenote to whisper words of love over the open flowers of the divine lotus.

Mayan Legends
ZAMNÁ
The Discovery of Henequen

Many years ago, where the city of Izamal now stands, a group of pilgrims called the Itzaes came to rest. They had sailed and walked long distances to arrive at this place, but their hearts were at peace because a good, wise priest known as *Zamná* guided them.

The women and children were exhausted so *Zamná* ordered a rest for everyone and sat on a rock. As he rested he remembered the star-filled night when the Queen of the continent Atlante, land of giants, silently came to him and spoke a prophecy.

"*Zamná*, I have told you that you are the best and wisest priest in my kingdom, and for this reason I have chosen you. My astronomers have read the skies and say that our land will disappear when the next moon comes.

"I want you to choose a group of families from my kingdom and the three wisest Chilames, or sacred scribes, to carry the writings that tell the story of our people and write what will happen in the future.

"You will come to a place that I will show you and there you will found a city. Under the main temple you will guard the writings of the past and those yet to be written, to conserve the history of Atlante.

"You and the chosen few will leave in nine canoes and sail west.
Nine days later you will find a land with no rivers or mountains and
you will land there. When you find water, that is where you will
found the city."

After sailing for two days, the sea was peaked with waves so high that two of the canoes sank. The land they were leaving was covered with a dark, lightening-filled sky. *Zamná* thought it the end of his country, just as the goddess had pronounced.

Zamná did arrive at the land without rivers or mountains, the land
the goddess had told him of. He did not, however, find the water he
needed, just an abundance of a plant with hard, lance-like leaves and
piercing spines.

As *Zamná* rested on the rock, the skies darkened and an endless rain began to fall. The pilgrims danced happily to celebrate the water the skies showered upon them.

Zamná got up from the rock to search for a place to store the rainwater. But in his search he was stabbed by one of these plants and a spine lodged in his leg with a painful jab.

His leg began to bleed. The Itzaes became angry at the plant and punished it by cutting off its leaves and pounding them against the endless rock of this land.

Zamná quickly realized that very resistant fibers came out of the pounded leaves, fibers that could be very useful to his people. He then knew that his wound was a sign for him to know this wonderful plant. He ordered the punishment to stop and thanked the gods for the discovery.

The rain continued, and the water quickly ran over the ground as if attracted to a certain place. *Zamná* followed the water until he came upon a hole into which the water fell. This was the place the goddess had indicated.

It was here that the good and wise Zamná, joining rain, the power of the sky, the spiny henequen and the strength of man, founded the great city of Izamal in an era long since lost in time.

THE XTABAY
Page...9

NICTE HÁ
LOTUS FLOWER
Page...57

ZAMNÁ
THE DISCOVERY OF HENEQUEN
Page...73

MAQUECH

Page...25

THE DWARF OF UXMAL

Page...41